EVOLUTION THEORY & ISLAM

(*Letter to Suleman Ali*)

Nuh Ha Mim Keller

MUSLIM ACADEMIC TRUST

The Muslim Academic Trust
Chetwynd House,
Bartlow, Cambridge CB1 6PP
United Kingdom

ISBN 1-902350-03-0

DESIGNED BY ABD AL-LATEEF WHITEMAN

Printed in Great Britain

Evolution Theory & Islam

Letter to Suleman Ali
14 July 1995
Dear Suleman Ali:
Thank you for your fax of 27 June 1995 which said, in part:

> Recently a pamphlet has been circulated around Oxford saying that 'evolution is synonymous with *kufr* and *shirk*.' I myself am a biologist and am convinced by the evidence which supports the theory of evolution. I am writing to ask whether the Quranic account of Creation is incompatible with man having evolved. Are there any books which you would recommend on the subject?

DURING MY 'logic of scientific explanation' period at the University of Chicago, I used to think that scientific theories had to have coherence, logicality, applicability, and adequacy, and I was accustomed to examine theory statements by looking at these things in turn. Perhaps they furnish a reasonable point of departure to give your question an answer which, if cursory and somewhat personal, may yet shed some light on the issues you raise.

Coherence

It seems to me that the very absoluteness of the theory's conclusions tends to compromise its 'objective' character. It is all very well to speak of the 'evidence of evolution,' but if the theory is thorough going, then *human consciousness* itself is also governed by evolution. This means that the categories that allow observation statements to arise as 'facts', categories such as number, space, time, event, measurement, logic, causality, and so forth, are mere physiological accidents of *random mutation* and *natural selection* in a particular species, *homo sapiens*. They have not come from any scientific considerations, but rather have arbitrarily arisen in man by blind and fortuitous evolution for the purpose of preserving the species.

I

They need not reflect external reality, 'the way nature is,' objectively, but only to the degree useful in preserving the species. That is, nothing guarantees the primacy, the objectivity, of these categories over others that would presumably have arisen had our consciousness evolved along different lines, such as those of more distant aquatic or subterranean species. The cognitive basis of every statement within the theory thus proceeds from the unreflective, unexamined historical forces that produced 'consciousness' in one species, a cognitive basis that the theory nevertheless generalizes to the whole universe of theory state-ments (the explanation of the origin of species) without explaining what permits this generalization. The pretences of the theory to correspond to an objective order of reality, applicable in an absolute sense to all species, are simply not compatible with the consequences of a thoroughly evolutionary viewpoint, which entails that the human cognitive categories that underpin the theory are purely relative and species-specific. The absolutism of random mutation and natural selection as explanative principles ends in eating the theory. With all its statements simultaneously absolute and relative, objective and subjective, generalizable and ungeneralizable, scientific and species-specific, the theory runs up on a reef of methodological incoherence.

Logicality

Speaking for myself, I was convinced that the evolution of man was an unchal-lengeable 'given' of modern knowledge until I read Charles Darwin's *Origin of Species.* The ninth chapter[1] made it clear, from what Darwin modestly calls the 'great imperfection of the geological record', that the theory *was not in principle falsifiable,* though the possibility that some kind of evidence or another should be able in principle to disprove a theory is a condition (if we can believe logicians like Karl Popper) for it to be considered scientific. By its nature, fossil evidence of intermediate forms that could prove or disprove the theory remained unfound and unfindable. When I read this, it was not clear to me how such an theory could be called 'scientific'.

If evolution is not scientific, then what is it? It seems to me that it is a human interpretation, an endeavour, an industry, a literature, based on what the American philosopher Charles Peirce called *abductive reasoning,* which functions in the following way:

(1) Suprising fact A.

(2) If theory B were the case, then A would naturally follow.

(3) Therefore B.

Here, (1) alone is certain, (2) is merely probable (as it explains the facts, though does not preclude other possible theories), while (3) has only the same probability as (2). If you want to see how ironclad the case for the evolution of man is, make a list of all the fossils discovered so far that 'prove' the evolution of man from lower life forms, date them, and then ask yourself if abductive reasoning is not what urges it, and if it really precludes the possibility of quite a different (2) in place of the theory of evolution.

Applicability

Is the analogy from *micro-evolution* within a species (which is fairly well-attested to by breeding horses, pigeons, useful plant hybrids, and so on) applicable to *macro-evolution,* from one species to another? That is, is there a single example of one species actually evolving into another, with the intermediate forms represented in the fossil record?

In the 1970s, Peter Williamson of Harvard University, under the direction of Richard Leakey, examined 3,300 fossils from excavations around Lake Turkana in Kenya, spanning several million years of the history of thirteen species of mollusks, that seemed to provide clear evidence of evolution from one species to another. He published his findings five years later in *Nature* magazine, and *Newsweek* picked up the story:

> Though their existence provides the basis for paleontology, fossils have always been something of an embarrassment to evolutionists. The problem is one of 'missing links': the fossil record is so littered with gaps that it takes a truly expert and imaginative eye to discern how one species could have evolved into another. [...] But now, for the first time, excavations at Kenya's Lake Turkana have provided clear fossil evidence of evolution from one species to another. The rock strata there contain a series of fossils that show every small step of an evolutionary journey that seems to have proceeded in fits and starts.[2]

Without dwelling on the *facticity* of scientific hypotheses raised under *logic* above, or that 3,300 fossils of thirteen species only 'cover' several million years if we already acknowledge that evolution is happening and are merely trying to see where the fossils fit in, or that we are back to Peirce's abductive reasoning here, although with a more probable minor premise because of the fuller geological record—that is, even if we grant that evolution is the 'given' which the fossils 'prove', an interesting point about the fossils (for a theist) is that the change was much more rapid than the traditional Darwinian mechanisms of random mutation and natural selection would warrant:

> What the record indicated was that the animals stayed much the same for immensely long stretches of time. But twice, about 2 million years ago and and then again 700,000 years ago, the pool of life seemed to explode—set off, apparently, by a drop in the lake's water level. In an instant of geologic time, as the changing lake environment allowed new types of mollusks to win the race for survival, all of the species evolved into varieties sharply different from their ancestors. Such sudden evolution had been observed before. What made the Lake Turkana fossil record unique, says Williamson, is that 'for the first time we see intermediate forms' between the old species and the new.

> That intermediate forms appeared so quickly, with new species suddenly evolving in 5,000 to 50,000 years after millions of years of constancy, challenges the traditional theories of Darwin's disciples. Most scientists describe evolution as a gradual process, in which random genetic mutations slowly produce new species. But the fossils of Lake Turkana don't record any gradual change; rather, they seem to reflect eons of stasis interrupted by brief evolutionary 'revolutions'.[3]

Of what significance is this to Muslims? In point of religion, if we put our scientific scruples aside for a moment and grant that evolution is *applicable* to something in the real world; namely, the mollusks of Lake Turkana, does this constitute unbelief (*kufr*) by the standards of Islam? I don't think so. Classic works of Islamic ʿ*aqīda* or 'tenets of faith' such as *Matn al-Sanūsiyya* tell us, 'As for what is possible in relation to Allah, it consists of His doing or not doing anything that is possible'.[4] That is, the omnipotent power of Allah can do anything that is not *impossible*, meaning either:

(a) intrinsically impossible (*mustaḥīl dhātī*), such as 'creating a five-sided triangle'—which is a mere confusion of words, and not something in any sense *possible*, such that we could ask whether Allah could do it;

(b) or else impossible because Allah has informed us that it shall not occur (*mustaḥīl ʿaraḍī*), whether He does so in the Koran, or through the Prophet ﷺ in a *mutawātir* hadith, meaning one that has reached us through so many means of transmission that it is impossible its transmitters could have all conspired to forge it. This category of the impossible is not impossible to begin with, but becomes so by the revelation from Allah, who is truthful and veracious. For example, it is impossible that Abū Lahab should be of the people of paradise, because the Koran

4

tells us he is of the people of hell (Koran 111).

With respect to evolution, the knowledge claim that Allah has brought one sort of being out of another is not *intrinsically* impossible ((a) above) because it is not self-contradictory. And as to whether it is (b), 'impossible because Allah has informed us that it cannot occur,' it would seem to me that we have two different cases, that of man, and that of the rest of creation.

Man

Regarding your question whether the Koranic account of creation is incompatible with man having evolved; if evolution entails, as Darwin believed, that 'probably all the organic beings which have ever lived on this earth have descended from one primordial form, into which life was first breathed',[5] I apprehend that this is incompatible with the Koranic account of creation. Our first ancestor was the prophet Adam (upon whom be peace), who was created by Allah in *janna,* or 'paradise' and not on earth, and was also created in a particular way that He describes to us:

> And when your Lord said to the angels, 'Truly, I will create a man from clay. So when I have completed him, and breathed into him of My spirit, then fall down prostrate to him.' And the angels prostrated, one and all. Save for Satan, who was too proud, and disbelieved. He said to him, 'O Satan, what prevented you from prostrating to what I have created with My two hands? Are you arrogant, or too exalted?' He said, 'I am better than he; You created me from fire and created him from clay'. (Koran 38:71–76)

Now, the God of Islam is transcendently above any suggestion of anthropomorphism, and Koranic exegetes like Fakhr al-Dīn al-Rāzī explain the above words *created with My two hands* as a figurative expression of Allah's special *concern* for this particular creation, the first human, since a sovereign of immense majesty does not undertake any work 'with his two hands' unless it is of the greatest importance.[6] I say 'the first human,' because the Arabic term *bashar* used in the verse 'Truly, I will create *a man* from clay' means precisely a human being and has no other lexical significance.

The same interpretive considerations (of Allah's transcendance above the attributes of created things) apply to the words *and breathed into him of My spirit.* Because the Koran unequivocally establishes that Allah is *Aḥad* or 'One', and is not an entity divisible into parts, exegetes say this 'spirit' was a *created* one, and that its attribution to Allah (*'My* spirit') is what is called in Arabic *iḍāfat al-tashrīf* 'an

5

attribution of honour,' showing that the *rūḥ* or 'spirit' within this first human being and his descendants was 'a sacred, exalted, and noble substance'[7]—not that there was a 'part of Allah' such as could enter into Adam's body, for that is unbelief. Similar attributions are not infrequent in Arabic, just as the Ka'ba is called *bayt Allāh,* or 'the House of Allah,' meaning 'Allah's honoured house,' not that it is His address; or such as the she-camel sent to the people of Thamūd, which was called *nāqat Allāh,* or 'the she-camel of Allah,' meaning 'Allah's honored she-camel,' signifying its inviolability in the *sharī'a* of the time, not that He rode it; and so on.

All of which shows that, according to the Koran, human beings are intrinsically—by their celestial provenance in *janna,* by their specially created nature, and by the *rūḥ* or spirit within them—at a quite different level in Allah's eyes than other terrestrial life, whether or not their bodies have certain physiological affinities with it, which are the prerogative of their Maker to create. Darwin says:

> I believe that animals have descended from at most only four or five progenitors, and plants from an equal or lesser number. Analogy would lead me one step further, namely, to the belief that all animals and plants have descended from some one prototype. But analogy may be a deceitful guide.[8]

Indeed it may. It is the nature of the place in which Allah has created us, this world (*dunyā*), that the possibility exists to deny the existence of Allah, His angels, His Books, His messengers, the Last Day, and destiny, its good and evil. If these things were not hidden by a veil, there would be no point in Allah's making us *responsible* for believing them. Belief would be involuntary, like the belief, say, that France is in Europe.

But what He has made us responsible for is precisely belief in the *unseen.* Why? In order that the divine names—such as *al-Rāfi'* or 'He Who Raises,' *al-Khāfiḍ,* 'He Who Abases,' *al-Mu'ṭī,* 'He Who Gives,' *al-Māni',* 'He Who Withholds,' *al-Raḥīm,* 'the Merciful,' *al-Muntaqim,* 'the Avenger,' *al-Laṭīf,* 'the Subtly Kind,' and so on—may be manifest.

How are they manifest? Only through the levels of human felicity and perdition, of salvation and damnation, by the disparity of human spiritual attainment in all its degrees: from the profound certitude of the prophets (upon whom be peace), to the faith of the ordinary believer, to the doubts of the waverer or hypocrite, to the denials of the damned. Also, the veil for its part has a *seamless* quality. To some, it is a seamless veil of light manifesting the Divine through the

6

perfection of creation; while to others, it is a seamless veil of darkness, a perfect nexus of interpenetrating causal relations in which there is no place for anything that is not material. Allah says,

> Exalted in Grace is He in whose hand is dominion, and He has power over all things. Who created death and life to try you, as to which of you is better in works, and He is the All-powerful, the Oft-forgiving. And who created the seven heavens in layers; you see no disparity in the creation of the All-merciful. Return your glance: do you see any fissures? (67:1–3).

The last time I checked, the university scene was an atheistic subculture, of professors and students actively or passively convinced that God was created by man. In bastions of liberalism like the University of California at Berkeley, for example, which still forbids the establishment of a Religions Department, only this attitude will do; anything else is immature, is primitivism. The reduction of human behavior to evolutionary biology is a major journalistic missionary outreach of this movement. I am pleased with this, inasmuch as Allah has created it to try us, to distinguish the good from the bad, the bad from the worse. But I don't see why Muslims should accept it as an explanation of the origin of man, especially when it contradicts what we know from the Creator of Man.

Other Species

As for other cases, change from one sort of thing to another does not seem to contradict revelation, for Allah says,

> O people! Fear your Lord, who created you from one soul [Adam, upon whom be peace] and *created from it* its mate [his wife Hawwā'], and spread forth from them many men and women, (4:1)

and also says, concerning the metamorphosis of a disobedient group of Banī Isrā'īl into apes,

> When they were too arrogant to [desist from] what they had been forbidden, We said to them, 'Be you apes, humiliated' (7:166).

and in a hadith,

> There shall be groups of people from my community who shall consider fornication, silk, wine, and musical instruments to be lawful: groups shall camp beside a high mountain, whom a shepherd returning to in the evening with one of their herds shall

7

approach for something he needs, and they shall tell him, 'Come back tomorrow.' Allah shall destroy them in the night, bringing down the mountain upon them, and transforming others into apes and swine until the Day of Judgement.[9]

Most Islamic scholars have understood these transformations literally, which shows that Allah's changing one thing into another (again, apart from the origin of man specifically) has not been traditionally considered to be contrary to the teachings of Islam. Indeed, the daily miracle of nutrition, the sustenance Allah provides for His creatures, in which one creature is transformed into another by being eaten, may be seen in the food chains that make up the economy of our natural world, as well as in our own plates.

If, as in the theory of evolution, we conjoin with this possibility the factors of causality, gradualism, mutation, and adaptation, it does not seem to me to add anything radically different to these other forms of change. For Islamic tenets of faith do not deny causal relations as such, but rather deny that *causes have effects in and of themselves,* for to believe this is to ascribe a co-sharer to Allah in His actions. Whoever believes in this latter causality (as virtually all evolutionists do) is an unbeliever (*kāfir*) without any doubt, as 'whoever denies the existence of ordinary causes has made the Wisdom of Allah Most High inoperative, while whoever attributes *effects* to them has associated co-sharers (*shirk*) to Allah Most High'.[10] As for Muslims, they believe that Allah alone creates causes, Allah alone creates effects, and Allah alone conjoins the two. In the words of the Koran, 'Allah is the Creator of everything'. (13:16)

A Muslim should pay careful attention to this point, and distance himself from believing either that causes (a) bring about effects in and of themselves; or (b) bring about effects in and of themselves through a capacity Allah has placed in them. Both of these negate the oneness and soleness (*waḥdāniyya*) of Allah, which entails that Allah has no co-sharer in:

(1) His entity (*dhāt*);

(2) His attributes (*ṣifāt*);

(3) or in His acts (*afʿāl*), which include the creation of the universe and everything in it, including all its causal relationships.

This third point is negated by both (a) and (b) above, and perhaps this is what your pamphleteer at Oxford had in mind when he spoke about the *shirk* (ascribing a co-sharer to Allah) of evolution theory.

In this connection, evolution as a knowledge claim about a causal relation does not seem to me intrinsically different from other similar knowledge claims, such as the statement 'The president died from an assassin's bullet.' Here, though in reality Allah alone gives life or makes to die, we find a dispensation in Sacred Law to speak in this way, provided that we know and believe that Allah alone brought about this effect. As for someone who literally believes that the bullet gave the president death, such a person is a *kāfir*. In reality he knows no more about the world than a man taking a bath who, when the water is cut off by the municipality, gets angry at the tap.

To summarize the answer to your question thus far: belief in macro-evolutionary transformation and variation of non-human species does not seem to me to entail *kufr* (unbelief) or *shirk* (ascribing co-sharers to Allah) unless one also believes that such transformation came about by *random* mutation and *natural* selection, understanding these adjectives as meaning causal independence from the will of Allah. You have to look in your heart and ask yourself what you believe. From the point of view of *tawḥīd*, Islamic theism, nothing happens 'at random,' there is no 'autonomous nature,' and anyone who believes in either of these is necessarily beyond the pale of Islam.

Unfortunately, this seems to be exactly what most evolutionists think. In America and England, they are the ones who write the textbooks, which raises weighty moral questions about sending Muslim students to schools to be taught these atheistic premises as if they were 'givens of modern science.' Teaching unbelief (*kufr*) to Muslims as though it were a fact is unquestionably unlawful. Is this unlawfulness mitigated (made legally permissible by *sharīᶜa* standards) by the need (*ḍarūra*) of upcoming generations of Muslims for scientific education? If so, the absence of textbooks and teachers in most schools who are conversant and concerned enough with the difficulties of the theory of evolution to accurately present its hypothetical character, places a moral obligation upon all Muslim parents. They are obliged to monitor their children's Islamic beliefs and to explain to them (by means of themselves, or someone else who can) the divine revelation of Islam, together with the difficulties of the theory of evolution that will enable the children to make sense of it from an Islamic perspective and understand which aspects of the theory are rejected by Islamic theism and which are acceptable. The question of the theory's *adequacy*, meaning its generalizability to all species, will necessarily be one of the important aspects of this explanation.

Adequacy

Of all the premises of evolution, the two that we have characterized above as unbelief (*kufr*); namely, *random* mutation and *natural* selection, interpreted in a

9

materialistic sense, are what most strongly urge its generalization to man. Why must we accept that man came from a common ancestor with animal primates, particularly since a fossil record of intermediate forms is not there? The answer of our age seems to be: 'Where else should he have come from?'

It is only if we accept the premise that there is no God that this answer acquires any cogency. The Koran answers this premise in detail and with authority. But evolutionary theory is not only ungeneralizable because of Allah informing us of His own existence and man's special creation, but because of what we discern in ourselves of the uniqueness of man, as the Koran says:

> We shall show them Our signs on the horizons and in themselves, until it is plain to them that it is the Truth (41:53).

Among the greatest of these signs in man's self is his birthright as *Khalīfa al-Raḥmān,* 'the successor of the All-merciful.' If it be wondered what this successorship consists in, the ulama of *taṣawwuf,* Islamic spirituality, have traditionally answered that it is to be looked for in the *maʿrifa bi'Llāh* or 'knowledge of Allah' that is the prerogative of no other being in creation besides the believer, and which is attained through following the path of inward purification, by strengthening the heart's attachment to Allah through acts of obedience specified by Sacred Law, particularly that of *dhikr.*

The locus of this attachment and this knowledge is not the mind, but rather the subtle faculty within one that is sometimes called the heart, and sometimes the *rūḥ* or spirit. Allah's special creation of this faculty has been mentioned above in connection with the Koranic words *and breathed into him of My spirit.* According to masters of the spiritual path, this subtle body is knowledgeable, aware, and cognizant, and when fully awakened, capable of transcending the opacity of the created universe to know Allah. The Koran says about it, by way of exalting its true nature through its very unfathomability: 'Say: The spirit is of the matter of my Lord.' (17:85)

How does it know Allah? I once asked this question of one of the ulama of *taṣawwuf* in Damascus, and recorded his answer in an unpublished manuscript. He told me:

> Beholding the Divine (*mushāhada*) is of two sorts, that of the eye and that of the heart. In this world, the beholding of the heart is had by many of the *ʿārifīn* (knowers of Allah), and consists of looking at contingent things, created beings, that they do not exist through themselves, but rather exist through Allah, and when the greatness of

Allah occurs to one, contingent things dwindle to nothing in one's view, and are erased from one's thought, and the Real (al-Ḥaqq) dawns upon one's heart, and it is as if one *beholds*. This is termed 'the beholding of the heart.' The beholding of the eye [in this world] is for the Chosen One, the Prophet alone, Muḥammad (Allah bless him and give him peace). As for the next world, it shall be for all believers. Allah Most High says, 'On that day faces shall be radiant, gazing upon their Lord.' (75:22)

[I wrote of the above:] If it be observed that the term *heart* as used above does not seem to conform to its customary usage among speakers of the language, I must grant this. In the context, the term denotes not the mind, but rather the faculty that perceives what is beyond created things, in the world of the spirit, which is a realm unto itself. If one demands that the existence of this faculty be demonstrated, the answer—however legitimate the request—cannot exceed, 'Go to masters of the discipline, train, and you will be shown.' Unsatisfying though this reply may be, it does not seem to me to differ in principle from answers that would be given, for example, to a nonspecialist regarding the proof for a particular proposition in theoretical physics or symbolic logic. Nor are such answers an objection to the in-principle 'publicly observable' character of observation statements in these disciplines, but rather a limitation pertaining to the nature of the case and the questioner, one that he may accept, reject, or do something about.[11]

Mere imagination? On the contrary, everything *besides* this knowledge is imagination, for the object of this knowledge is Allah, true reality, which cannot be transient but is unchanging, while other facts are precisely imaginary. The child you used to be, for example, exists now only in your imagination; the person who ate your breakfast this morning no longer exists except in your imagination; your yesterday, your tomorrow, your today (except, perhaps, for the moment you are presently in, which has now fled): all is imaginary, and only hypostatized as phenomenal reality, as unity, as facticity, as real—through imagination. Every moment that comes is different, winking in and out of existence, preserved in its relational continuum by pure imagination, which constitutes it as 'world'. What we notice of this world is thus imaginary, like what a sleeper sees. In this connection, ʿAlī ibn Abī Ṭālib (God ennoble his countenance) has said, 'People are asleep, and when they die, they wake up.'[12]

This is not to denigrate the power of imagination; indeed, but for imagination, we could not believe in the truths of the afterlife, paradise, hell, and everything that our eternal salvation depends upon. Rather, I mention this in the context of the question of evolution as a cautionary note against a sort of 'fallacy of misplaced concrescence,' an unwarranted epistemological overconfidence, that exists in many people who work in what they term 'the hard sciences.'

As someone from the West, I was raised from early school years as a believer not only in *science,* the practical project of discovery that aims at exploiting more and more of the universe by identification, classification, and description of micro–and macro–causal relations; but also in *scientism,* the belief that this enterprise constitutes absolute knowledge. As one philosopher whom I read at the University of Chicago put it,

> Scientism is science's belief in itself: that is, the conviction that we can no longer understand science as one form of possible knowledge, but rather must identify knowledge with science.[13]

It seems to me that this view, in respect to evolution but also in respect to the nature of science as a contemporary religion, represents a sort of defeat of knowledge by an absolutism of pure methodology. As I mentioned at the outset, the categories of understanding that underly every observation statement in the theory of evolution arise from human consciousness, and as such cannot be distinguished by the theory from other transient survival devices: its explanative method, from first to last, is necessarily only another survival mechanism that has evolved in the animal kingdom. By its own measure, it is not necessary that it be true, but only necessary that it be powerful in the struggle for survival. Presumably, any other theory—even if illusory—that had better implications for survival could displace evolution as a mode of explanation. Or perhaps the theory itself is an illusion.

These considerations went through my mind at the University of Chicago during my 'logic of scientific explanation' days. They made me realize that my faith in scientism and evolutionism had something magical as its basis, the magic of an influential interpretation supported by a vast human enterprise. I do not propose that science should seriously try to comprehend itself, which in any case it is not equipped to do, but I have come to think that, for the sake of its consumers, it might have the epistemological modesty to 'get back' from its current scientistic pretentions to its true nature, as one area of human interpretation among others. From being the 'grand balance scale' on which one may weigh and judge the 'reality' of all matters, large and small—subsuming 'the concept of God,' for example, under the study of religions, religions under anthropology, anthropology under human behavioral institutions, human behavioral institutions under evolutionary biology, evolutionary biology under organic chemistry, organic chemistry (ultimately) under cosmology, cosmology under chaos theory, and so on—I have hopes that science will someday get back to its true role, the production of technically exploitable knowledge for human life. That is, from pretentions to ʿilm or 'knowledge', to its true role as fann or 'technique'.

In view of the above considerations of its coherence, logicality, applicability, and adequacy, the theory of the evolution of man from lower forms does not seem to show enough scientific rigour to raise it from the status of a mere influential interpretation. To show evolution's *adequacy* for everything it is trying to explain would be to give valid grounds to generalize it to man. In this respect, it is a little like Sigmund Freud's *Interpretation of Dreams,* in which he describes examples of dreams that are wish fulfillments, and then concludes that 'all dreams are wish fulfillments'. We still wait to be convinced.

Summary of Islamic Conclusions

Allah alone is Master of Existence. He alone causes all that is to be and not to be. Causes are without effect in themselves, but rather both cause and effect are created by Him. The causes and the effects of all processes, including those through which plant and animal species are individuated, are His work alone. To ascribe efficacy to anything but His action, whether believing that causes (a) bring about effects in and of themselves; or (b) bring about effects in and of themselves through a capacity Allah has placed in them, is to ascribe associates to Allah (*shirk*). Such beliefs seem to be entailed in the literal understanding of 'natural selection' and 'random mutation', and other evolutionary concepts, unless we understand these processes as *figurative* causes, while appreciating that Allah alone is the agent. This is aside from the consideration of whether they are true or not.

As for the claim that man has evolved from a nonhuman species, this is unbelief (*kufr*) irrespective of whether we ascribe the process to Allah or to 'nature', because it negates the truth of Adam's special creation revealed in the Koran. Man is of special origin, as is attested not only by revelation, but also by the divine secret within him, the capacity for maʿrifa or knowledge of the Divine that he alone of all creatures possesses. By his God-given nature, man stands before a door opening onto infinitude that no other creature in the universe can aspire to. Man is something else.

Further Reading

—Michael Denton. *Evolution: A Theory in Crisis*. Bethesda, Maryland: Adler and Adler Publishers, 1986. Originally published in Great Britain by Burnett Books Ltd. Discusses molecular genetics and other scientific aspects not examined above.

—*Encyclopedia of Ignorance*. Ed. Duncan Roland. Oxford: Pergamon Press, 1978.

—Ruqaiyyah Waris Maqsood. *Thinking About God*. Bloomington, Indiana: American Trust Publications.

—Shaikh Abdul Mabud, *The Theory of Evolution: An Assessment from the Islamic point of view*. Cambridge: Islamic Academy, 1991.

Notes

1 C. Darwin, *The Origin of Species by Means of Natural Selection, or The Preservation of Favoured Races in the Struggle for Life*, ed. J.W. Burrow, London: Penguin Books, 1979, 291–317

2 Sharon Begley and John Carey, 'Evolution: Change at a Snail's Pace,' *Newsweek*, 7 December 1981

3 ibid.

4 al-Sanūsī, *Umm al-barāhīn*, with the *Ḥāshiya* of al-Dasūqī. Cairo n.d. Reprint Beirut: Dar al-Fikr, n.d, 145–46

5 *The Origin of Species*, 455.

6 *Tafsīr al-Fakhr al-Rāzī*. 32 vols. Beirut 1401/1981. Reprint (32 vols. in 16), Beirut: Dar al-Fikr, 1405/1985, 26, 231–32.

7 ibid., 228.

8 *The Origin of Species*, 454–55.

9 *Ṣaḥīḥ al-Bukhārī*. 9 vols. Cairo 1313/1895. Reprint (9 vols. in 3), Beirut: Dar al-Jīl, n.d., 7, 138.

10 al-Hāshimī: *Miftāḥ al-janna fī sharḥ ʿaqīda Ahl al-Sunna*. Damascus: Maṭbaʿa al-taraqqī, 1379/1960, 33

11 Keller, *Interpreter's Log*.

12 al-Sakhāwī, *al-Maqāṣid al-Ḥasana*. Cairo 1375/1956. Reprint. Beirut: Dār al-kutub al-ʿilmiyya, 1399/1979, 442.

13 Jurgen Habermas, *Knowledge and Human Interests*. Tr. Jeremy J. Shapiro. Boston: Beacon Press, 1971, 4.

Thank you for asking me this question, which made me think about my own beliefs. I remain at your service, Nuh Ha Mim Keller.